C O S M O D I G I T A L
Wonder Series for Children

Moral Stories Retold
By
Jaspreet Gill

"Do not pretend to be who you are not"

You should never pretend to be who you are not. Pretending to be someone else might put you in undesirable situation. By pretending to be someone else you will never become that person. But you may lose the good qualities you may already have. Be yourself!

The Blue Fox

Illustrations
Jaspreet Gill

Once upon a time, in a forest, there lived a fox.

One morning he went for a walk in the forest.

He accidently wandered out of the forest and came across a small village.

Out of curiosity, he decided to go see what was in this village.

While walking in the village, he walked into one of the houses.

The woman who lived in this house was dyeing her clothes with colors.

While jumping around the fox tripped and fell into the tub with the blue dye.

When the fox came out of the tub, his entire fur coat had turned blue.

He was shocked at what had just happened.

He ran back into the forest as fast as he possibly could.

As he walked into the forest he thought, "Oh what a royal color I have. I appear fit to be the king of the forest". All his animal friends looked at his blue fur but did not recognize him.They believed the fox to be a royal creature they had never seen.

The fox began to brag and declared- "As blue is the color of Kings, this forest has made me your King!"

The word soon spread and everyone believed the fox to be the King of the forest.

All the animals in the forest bowed to the fox.

Even the lion believed the fox to be the king and began to attend to him.

The blue fox began to think highly of himself.

He avoided the other foxes because he thought he was better than them.

This angered the other foxes and made them sad.

One day the other foxes decided to go ask the wise fox for help.

They said to him, "The blue fox does not like us. We do know for sure that he is just a fox like us".

The wise fox told them what they should do.

According to the plan, the foxes sent up a loud howl.

When the blue fox heard the howl he howled back because it was in his nature.

The lion quickly realized that the fox had lied about himself being a King. He was just an ordinary fox with different color.

The lion kicked the fox out of the forest forever.

Moral

"Do not pretend to be who you are not"

You should never pretend to be who you are not. Pretending to be someone else might put you in undesirable situation. By pretending to be someone else you will never become that person. But you may lose the good qualities you already have. Be yourself!

Vocabulary Words

Dye: to color hair or fabric
Wander: casual/aimless walk
Curiosity: strong desire
Recognize: identify, to know
Brag: boast, self-praise
Declare: express, announce
Attend: to be present at
Avoid: keep oneself away from
Howl: a long loud or sound by dog or wolf

Made in the USA
Monee, IL
23 January 2021